Sandy

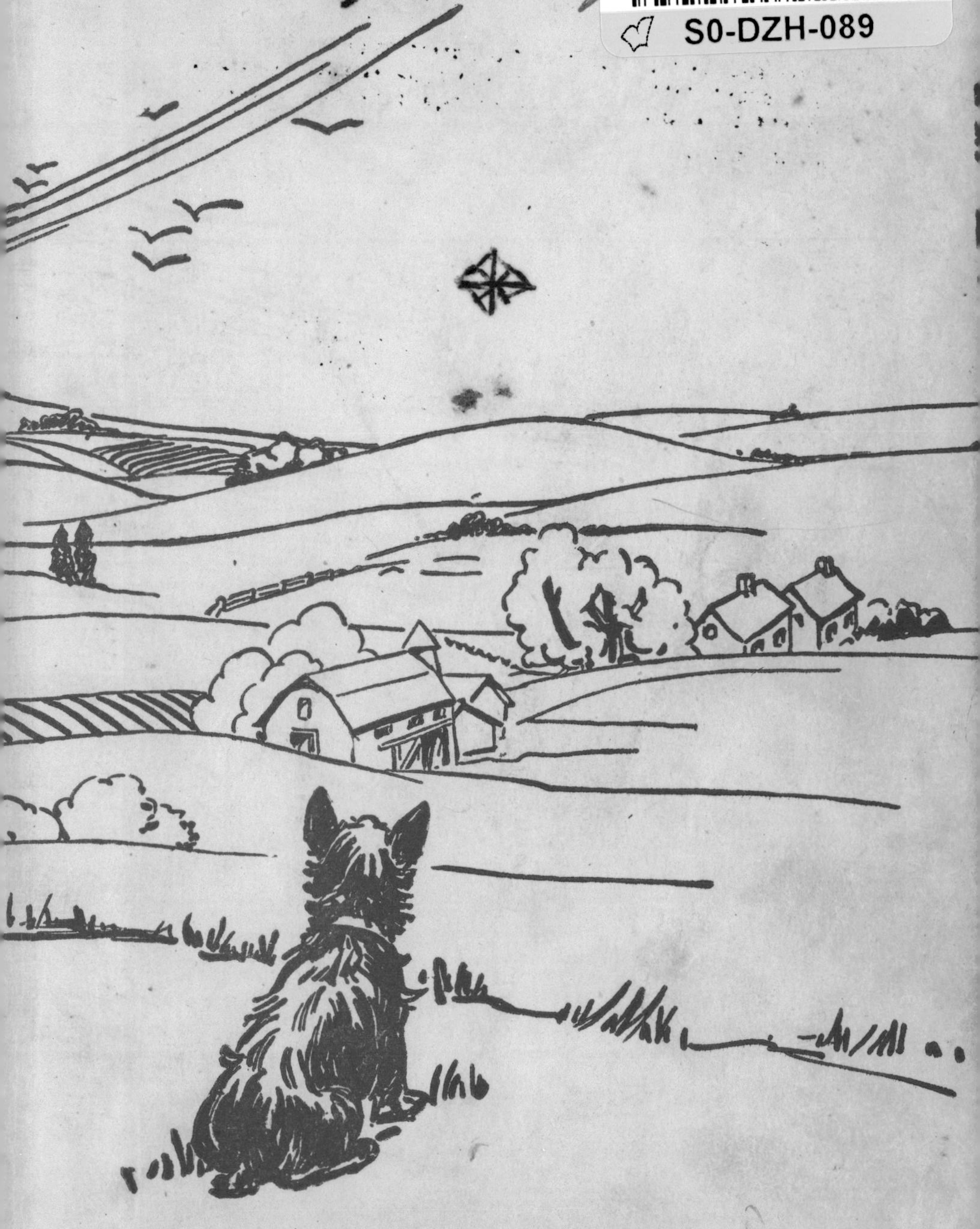

EASY GROWTH in READING

FIRST READER LEVEL ONE

I KNOW A SECRET

BY

GERTRUDE HILDRETH
TEACHERS COLLEGE, COLUMBIA UNIVERSITY

ALLIE LOU FELTON   MABEL J. HENDERSON
ALICE MEIGHEN

ILLUSTRATED BY
CORINNE PAULI WATERALL AND JACOB BATES ABBOTT

THE JOHN C. WINSTON COMPANY

COLLABORATING EDITORS

GRACE A. ALLEN
Assistant Director of Training
State Teachers College
Buffalo, New York

JOY MUCHMORE LACEY
Professor of Education
Indiana State Teachers College
Terre Haute, Indiana

EULA A. JOHNSTON
Elementary Supervisor
Hamilton County
Chattanooga, Tennessee

ETHEL MALTBY GEHRES
Author of Primary Readers
Philadelphia, Pennsylvania

CONTENTS

PLAY TIME

SNOW! SNOW!

SPRING IS HERE

SURPRISES

A BIRTHDAY

THE CIRCUS

BACK HOME AT THE FAR

PLAY TIME

Guess What Bob Has!

"Guess what I have!" said Bob.

"What is it?" said Nancy.

"It can walk," said Bob.

"It is little.

Guess what it is."

"Can it talk?" said Nancy.

1

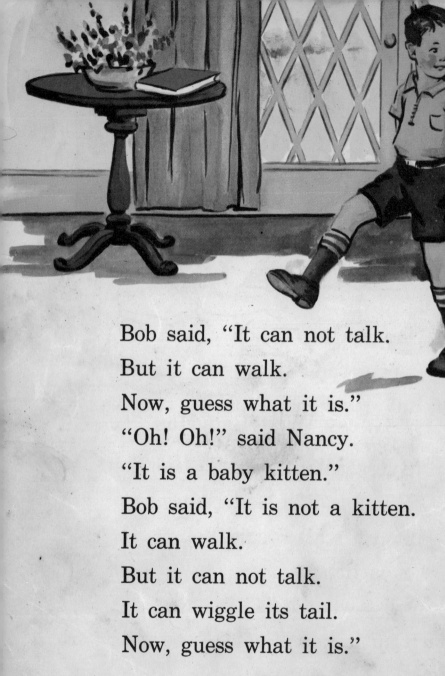

Bob said, "It can not talk.

But it can walk.

Now, guess what it is."

"Oh! Oh!" said Nancy.

"It is a baby kitten."

Bob said, "It is not a kitten.

It can walk.

But it can not talk.

It can wiggle its tail.

Now, guess what it is."

Nancy said, "What can it be?

It can walk.

But it can not talk.

It can wiggle its tail."

Bob said, "Guess again.

Guess again."

"Oh! I know," said Nancy.

"It is a baby rabbit.

Where is it?

I want to see it."

Bob said, "Guess again, Nancy.

It is not a baby rabbit.

It is not a baby kitten.

It can not talk.

But it can walk.

It can wiggle its tail.

And it can swim."

Nancy said, "It can swim!

Is it a turtle?"

4

Bob said, "It is not a turtle.
It is not a baby rabbit.
It is not a baby kitten.
Do you give up?"
Nancy said, "I can not guess.
I give up! I give up!
What is it?"
Bob said, "Come with me.
Come with me and you will see."
Nancy went with Bob.
And what did she see?

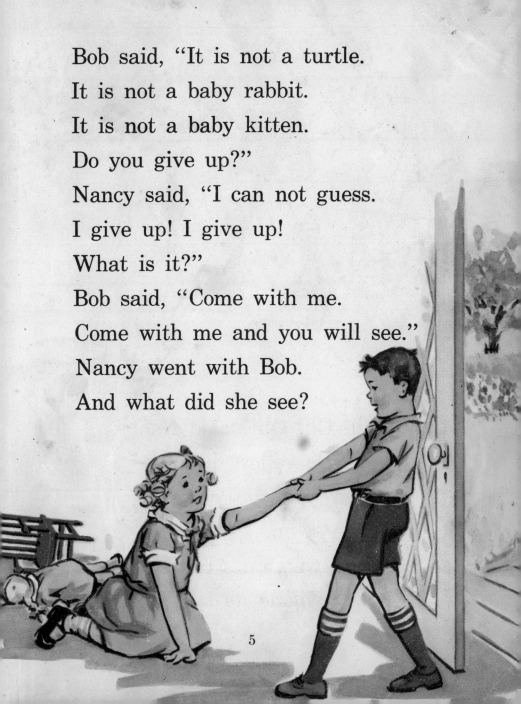

"Oh! Oh! Oh!" said Nancy.

"A little yellow duck!

It can walk.

It can swim.

It can wiggle its tail.

See it wiggle its tail!"

Here Are Tom and Don

Bob said, "We have a duck.

It came from the farm.

It came from Jack's farm.

It can wiggle its tail."

Don said, "Look at it now.

See it wiggle its tail."

Nancy said, "It can swim, too."

One puppy saw the duck.

He wanted to play with it.

But the duck ran away.

It was afraid of the puppy.

Tom said, "Go home, puppies!

The duck is afraid of you.

Go home and play."

Bob said, "Come, little duck.

Do not run away from me.

The puppies are going home."

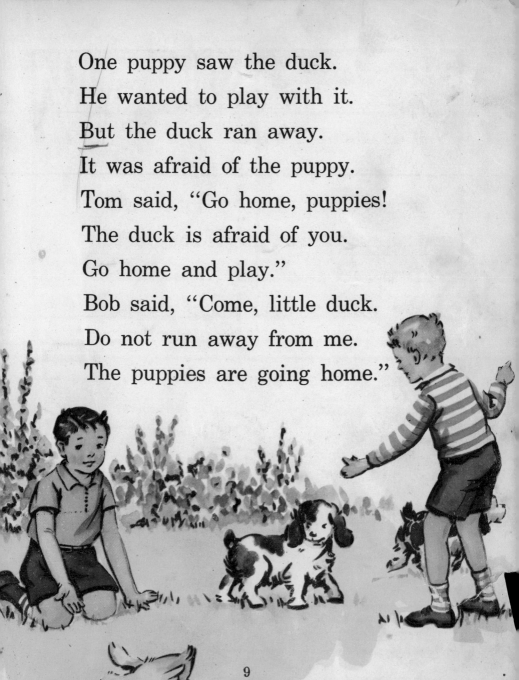

I Know a Story

Bob said, "I know a story.
It is about a duck.
Who wants to hear it?"
Nancy said, "I do! I do!
I want to hear about the duck."
Tom and Don said, "We do!
We want to hear about the duck."

This is Bob's story.

Yellow Duck's Corn

Yellow Duck had some corn.

Mrs. Hen saw the corn.

She said, "Cluck, cluck.

I will get Yellow Duck's corn."

She ran to Yellow Duck.

She said, "Give me some corn.

Give me some corn, Yellow Duck."

11

Yellow Duck said,
"This is my corn.
You had some corn.
You can not have my corn."
And away she ran with it.
Mrs. Hen said, "I can run fast.
I can run as fast as you can."

So she ran after Yellow Duck.

Yellow Duck saw a rabbit.
She said, "What can I do?
Mrs. Hen wants my corn.
What can I do?"
The rabbit said, "Run!
Run away from Mrs. Hen.
Then she can not catch you."
So Yellow Duck ran.
She ran as fast as she could.
But Mrs. Hen ran fast, too.

13

Then Yellow Duck saw a kitten.

She said, "What can I do?

Mrs. Hen wants my corn.

I am afraid she will catch me.

What can I do?"

The kitten said,

"Run fast! Run fast!

Then Mrs. Hen can not catch you."

So Yellow Duck ran fast.
She ran as fast as she could.
Mrs. Hen ran fast, too.
She ran as fast as she could.

Yellow Duck was crying.
She said, "Who will help me?
Mrs. Hen wants my corn."
Just then she saw a turtle.

The turtle said,
"Stop crying, Yellow Duck.
I will tell you what to do."
"Tell me!" said Yellow Duck.
"Tell me what to do."
Then the turtle said something.
Yellow Duck said, "Thank you!
I will stop crying.
I know what to do now."

And away she ran.

16

Yellow Duck laughed as she ran.

She came to some water.

She said, "Now I am not afraid.

Mrs. Hen can not catch me now.

She can not get my corn.

I will swim away with it."

Mrs. Hen saw Yellow Duck.

Yellow Duck was in the water.

She said, "Stop, Yellow Duck!"

But Yellow Duck did not stop.

She just laughed and laughed.

Did Mrs. Hen get the corn? NO

After the Story

Tom and Don went home.

Bob and Nancy played.

They played with their duck.

Nancy said, "Come, little duck.

The duck in the story can swim.

You can swim, too.

The duck in the story is yellow.

You are yellow, too."

Bob said, "Come, Yellow Duck.

We are going to feed you.

Mother will let us feed you."

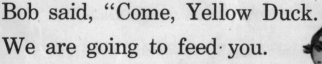

18

The Puppies at Home

The puppies will play at home.
They want their ball.
They want to play with it
They do not know where it is.
But they will look for it.

Tom said, "Oh! Mother!
Look at my puppy!"
Mother looked at Tom's puppy.
She laughed at him.
Tom and Don laughed, too.
Tom's puppy looked so funny.
He had on Father's hat.
Don's puppy had his ball.
He wanted to play with it.

Mother said, "Oh, puppies!
Go out! Go out!
You can not play in here."
Tom said, "Come, Don.
We will go out with them.
We will play with them."
The puppies ran out.
They were happy now.
Tom and Don were going to play.
They had their ball, too.

22

SNOW! SNOW!

Mother said, "Oh! See the snow!
Tomorrow will be cold."
Father said,
"What fun the boys will have.
This snow will make them happy.
They can play with their sleds.
They will have fun tomorrow.
The snow will be a surprise."

Fun in the Snow

Tom said, "Look, Don!
Just look at the snow!
Let us get our sleds out."
Don said, "Oh! Our sleds!
Our Christmas sleds!
We can ride on our sleds."
Tom and Don were happy.
They were happy to see the snow.
The puppies were happy.
The puppies wanted to go, too.
They will pull the sleds.

The Snow Man

Don said, "It was fun.

It was fun to ride on our sleds.

Let us make a snow man now."

Tom said, "Good! Good!

We can make a funny snow man.

We can put a long nose on him."

Don said, "Father will help us.

Father can make him look funny."

So they made a funny snow man.

They put a long nose on him.

They put Father's hat on him.

Don's puppy was afraid of him.

He was afraid to go near him.

He ran away from him.

Tom's puppy was not afraid.

He jumped at the snow man.

He jumped and jumped at him.

Bob and Nancy came.
Anne came with them.
They wanted to see the snow man.
Bob said, "See his long nose!
See his two black eyes.
The snow man is funny."
Nancy laughed and said,
"He has a funny hat."
Tom said, "Oh, Father!
Will the snow man stay with us?"

30.

The Sun's Joke

"Oh! Oh! Mr. Snow Man!
Oh! Oh!" said the sun.
"This is just what I wanted.
Now see me have fun."

"Oh! Stay! Mr. Snow Man!
Oh! Stay!" said the sun.
"The boys and girls want you.
They want to have fun."

Nancy and Bob came again.

Anne came with them.

They wanted to see the snow man.

Bob and Nancy laughed.

They said, "Oh, Mr. Snow Man!"

Anne said, "Where did he go?"

Bob said, "There is his nose.

There are his two black eyes.

See his two black eyes."

Father laughed and said,

"See what the sun did.

The sun played a good joke."

Spring is here!
Spring is here!
I know it!
I know it!
I know it!

33

The Bird House

"Look, Bob, look!" said Nancy.

"The birds are back.

The birds are back."

Bob said,

"All the birds will come back.

They will soon be here.

Let us make a house for them.

Father will help us."

Here is the bird house.
It is up in the tree.
Father and Bob made it.
Nancy said, "Come birds.
We want you to live here.
We want to feed you."
Father said, "They will come.
They will soon find the house."

The birds have come.

They saw Bob's bird house.

They have come to live in it.

They are happy.

Soon there will be some eggs.

Then there will be baby birds.

Bob and Nancy are happy.

They want the birds to stay.

They will feed them.

Rain! Rain!

Bob said, "Rain! Rain!
See the rain come down.
I like to see the rain."
Nancy said, "I like the rain.
I like to play in it.
May we go out, Mother?
May we play in the rain?"
Mother said, "You may.
You may play in the rain."

e did not want to go.

d not like the rain.

ted to play.

party for her dolls.

es on the table.

time she had!

she had with her dolls!

39

Play in the Rain

Nancy said, "What are you

Bob said, "I am a frog.

Ker-chug! Ker-chug!

I like the rain.

I like to play in the rain.

Ker-chug! Ker-chug!

I like to play in the water."

Ann

She di

She wan

She had a

She had cak

What a good

What fun

n

, Bob?"

Bob said, "What are you, Nancy?"

Nancy said, "I am a duck.

Quack, quack, quack, quack.

I like the rain.

I like to play in the rain.

Quack, quack, quack, quack.

I like to play in the water."

At School

Miss Hall's Book

Miss Hall has a pretty book.

We like her pretty book.

Her book is about spring.

It is about the birds.

She reads to us.

This is what she reads.

Singing in the Rain

I see a frog.

He is singing in the rain.

Ker-chug! Ker-chug!

Ker-chug! Ker-chug!

Spring is here!

Spring is here!

I know it!

I know it!

Ker-chug! Ker-chug!

Singing in a Tree

I see a robin.

He is up in a tree.

He is singing to you.

He is singing to me.

Spring is here!

Spring is here!

I know it!

I know it!

Two little robins up in a tree.
They made a nest as you can see.

Two little robins up in a tree.
Eggs in a nest as you can see.

46

Two little robins up in a tree.
They are happy as you can see.

Three baby robins up in a tree.
They want to fly as you can see.

Miss Hall said,
"It is time to go home now."
The girls said, "Oh, Miss Hall!
May we bring our dolls tomorrow?"
Miss Hall said, "Yes, you may.
You may bring your dolls.
The boys have made a play house.
You may bring your dolls.
You may play in the play house."

After School

Nancy and Bob ran home.

Nancy said, "Mother! Mother!

Where are you, Mother?"

Mother said, "Here I am.

Come here! Come here!"

Nancy put her books down.

She put her hat down, too.

She and Bob ran to Mother.

Bob said, "Oh, Mother!
May I have something to eat?"
Nancy said,
"May I have something, too?"
Mother said, "Yes, you may.
You may have something to eat.
We have some good apples.
You may have big red apples."

Where Is My Doll?

Nancy said, "Oh, Mother!
Where is my doll?
Miss Hall said we could bring
our dolls to school.
She said we could bring
them tomorrow."
Mother said,
"Look for your doll."
Bob said, "I will help you.
I will look for your doll.
You will have fun tomorrow."

51

Nancy and Bob looked and looked
for the doll.
They looked in the chairs.
They looked under the chairs.
They looked all around.
They could not find the doll.
Just then Bob saw something.
He said, "Look, Nancy!
Look at your hat!
Where is it going?"

Bob and Nancy laughed.
Nancy said, "Look, Bob!
Look at my hat!"
The hat went
this way
and that way
and this way
and that way.
Bob said, "What a good joke!
What a good joke on you!"

Nancy ran to her hat.

She said, "Come, Miss Muff!

You played a joke on me.

You were hiding under my hat.

My doll was hiding there, too.

I will put my hat away.

I will put it away after this.

I will put my doll away, too."

SURPRISES

Something Smells Good

Bob said,
"Something smells so good.
What is it, Nancy?"
Nancy said, "I do not know.
Come, we will see."
They ran to Mother.
Bob said, "Mother! Mother!
What is it that smells so good?"
Nancy said, "What have you made?
What have you made, Mother?"

Bob said, "It smells so good.
It smells just like apples.
I like apples."
Nancy said, "Oh! What is it?
Tell us what it is, Mother."
Mother said, "I can not tell.
This is a surprise.
You will see! You will see!"

Bob said, "It smells good.
I know it has apples in it.
It smells like something
good to eat."
Mother said, "It will be good.
It will be good to eat.
You will like it.
Run out and play.
Run out and play."

Nancy's Surprise

Bob ran out to play.

But Nancy did not go to play.

She said, "I know what I can do.

I can surprise Mother."

She tiptoed to the table.

She tiptoed and tiptoed

around and around the table.

What did Nancy do? She sat the table.

Nancy said, "Mother! Mother!
Come here, Mother.
I have a surprise for you.
Come and see my surprise."

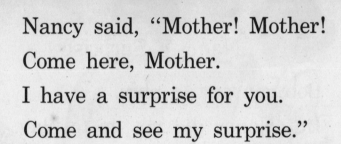

Mother said, "Oh, Nancy!
I like your surprise.
You will like my surprise, too.
It will be a good surprise."

Nancy and Father

Then Nancy saw Father
as he sat in his big chair.
Father did not see Nancy.
He did not know she was there.
Nancy tiptoed and tiptoed
to the back of his big chair.
Father did not see her.
He did not know she was there.

Father said, "What do I hear?
A knock, knock, knock
on the back of my chair!
Now who can it be?
Little Yellow Quack!"
"No," said a little voice.
Then Father said,
"Big funny Mac!"
"No! No!" said a big voice.

Knock, knock, knock!

"Oh, me! Oh, my!" said Father.

"Who is there?

Who hides at the back

of my chair?

Is it a big black bear?"

"No!" said a big, big voice.

Then Father said,

"Who can it be?

Let me see.

Now let me see.

Is it my little honey bee?"

"Yes," said a little voice
from the back of Father's chair.
And out jumped little Nancy,
for she was hiding there.
She said, "Tell me a story,
a good story about a bear!"
Father said in a big voice,
"This is the story
about the Good Little Bear!"

A Good Little Bear

Mother Bear was going away.

She put Baby Bear up in a tree.

She said, "Stay up in the tree.

Do not come down

until I come back."

Baby Bear wanted to go, too.

But he said, "I will stay here.

I will stay here

until you come back, Mother."

65

Baby Bear looked around.
He said, "I do not like
to stay up here.
I do not want to stay up here
until Mother comes back."
He looked around again.
He said, "I smell something.
It smells good, too.
It makes me wiggle my nose.
I will see what it is."
And he began to climb.

Bushy Tail came to the tree.
Bushy Tail was a squirrel.
He said, "Come down, Baby Bear.
Come down and play with me."
Baby Bear said, "Oh! No!
I can not come down
until my Mother comes back.
I smell something good.
I want to find out what it is."
Then Bushy Tail said,
"I will come up."
And Bushy Tail began to climb.

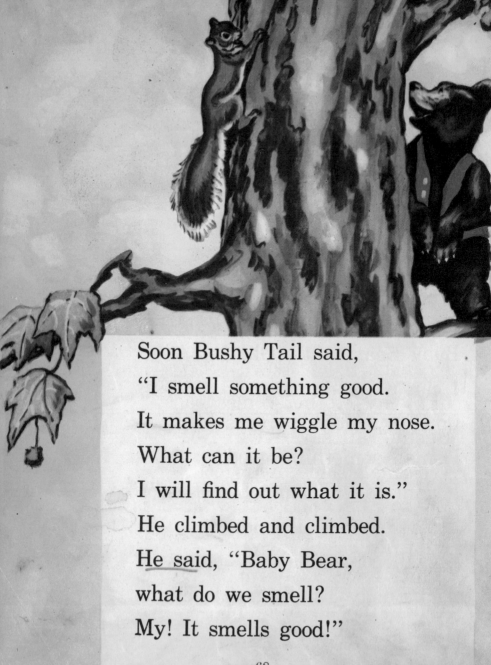

Soon Bushy Tail said,
"I smell something good.
It makes me wiggle my nose.
What can it be?
I will find out what it is."
He climbed and climbed.
He said, "Baby Bear,
what do we smell?
My! It smells good!"

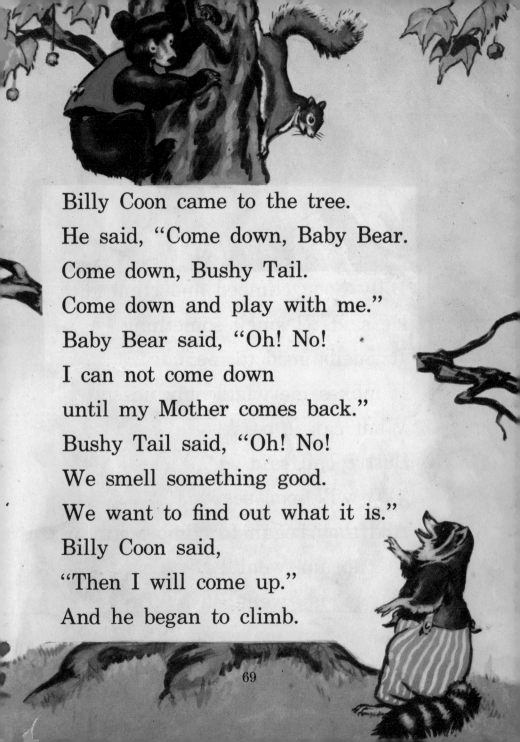

Billy Coon came to the tree.

He said, "Come down, Baby Bear.

Come down, Bushy Tail.

Come down and play with me."

Baby Bear said, "Oh! No!

I can not come down

until my Mother comes back."

Bushy Tail said, "Oh! No!

We smell something good.

We want to find out what it is."

Billy Coon said,

"Then I will come up."

And he began to climb.

Billy Coon climbed and climbed.
He said, "I smell something.
It smells good to me.
It makes me wiggle my nose.
What can it be?"
Bushy Tail said,
"We will soon see."
And they began to climb again.
Up, up, up, went Baby Bear.
Up, up, up, went Bushy Tail.
And up, up, up, went Billy Coon.

70

Billy Coon said,
"I smell honey!"
Bushy Tail said,
"I smell honey!"
Baby Bear said,
"I smell honey!"
"Where is it?" said Billy Coon.
"I know! I know!" said Baby Bear.
"See that big hole in the tree.
The honey may be in that hole.
We will see where it is."

Baby Bear tried and tried
to reach the hole.
But he could not reach it.
Billy Coon tried and tried.
He could not reach the hole.
Bushy Tail tried and tried.
He could not reach the hole.
The hole was too high.

Baby Bear said, "I know!
I will reach as high as I can.
Billy Coon can get on my back.
He can reach as high as he can.
Bushy Tail can get
on Billy Coon's back.
Bushy Tail can reach
as high as he can.
Then he can reach the hole."

So Billy Coon climbed up
on Baby Bear's back.
Bushy Tail climbed up
on Billy Coon's back.
Bushy Tail said, "I am up high.
I can reach the hole.
It is honey! It is honey!"
"Give me some," said Baby Bear.
"Give me some," said Billy Coon.

"Bees! Bees!" said Bushy Tail.

"Bees! Bees!" said Billy Coon.

"I want my Mother!"

said Baby Bear.

75

Baby Bear saw his Mother.

He began to cry.

He said, "Oh, Mother!

We wanted some honey.

Then all the bees came out.

Look at my eyes, Mother.

And look at Billy's nose."

Bushy Tail said, "I like honey.

But I do not like bees.

I am not going up there again."

Billy Coon said,

"I am going home, I am!"

Father said,

"Do you like my story?"

Nancy said, "It is a good story.

I like honey, too.

I do not like bees.

Where did Billy Coon go?

Where is his home?

Where did Bushy Tail go?

Did they get some honey?"

Dinner

Mother said, "Come to dinner.
Come to dinner.
We have something good.
It has apples in it."
Nancy said, "I know what it is.
I know what it is."
Bob said, "I know what it is."

After dinner Nancy said, "Father,
what did the little bear do?
What did all the bees do?"
Father said,
"Little Bear went for a walk.
He went for a long walk."
Nancy said, "Tell me about him.
Tell me about his walk."
Father said,
"I will read to you."

Little Bear's Walk in the Woods

Little Bear said, "Good-by!

Good-by, Mother.

I am going for a walk.

I am going out into the woods.

I want to find Bushy Tail.

I want to find Billy Coon.

I want to play with them."

Mother Bear said, "Good-by!

Come back to your dinner.

Good-by, good-by."

Little Bear was happy.

He was going to the woods.

He said,

"I like to play with Billy Coon.

I like to play with Bushy Tail.

I will stay away from the tree
with the big hole in it.

The bees are hiding in the hole.

I do not like bees.

I want to find Billy Coon.

I want to find Bushy Tail."

Little Bear looked around.
He looked around in the woods.
He said, "Where is Bushy Tail?
I can not find Bushy Tail.
I can not find Billy Coon.
But I am not afraid."
Just then he heard something.
It said, "Moo, moo, moo."
Little Bear said,
"What was that?
What was that?
Oh! I am not afraid!"

But up into a tree he went.
He looked down at the cow.
He said, "I am not hiding.
I just like to climb.
I am not afraid of cows."
The cow said, "Moo, moo, moo!"
Little Bear said, "Go away!
Go away, big cow!
I am not afraid of you."
And down from the tree
came Little Bear.

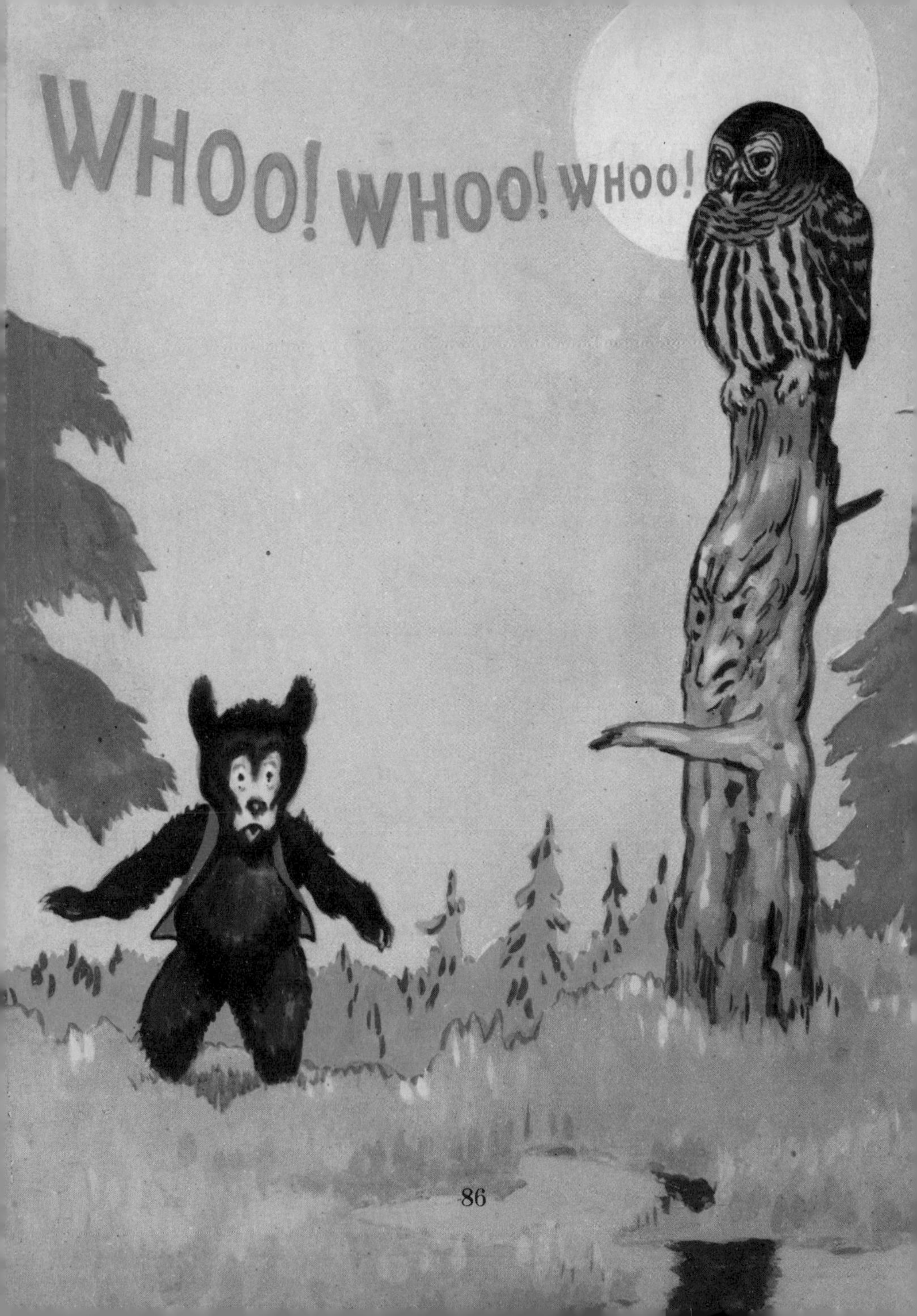
WHOO! WHOO! WHOO!

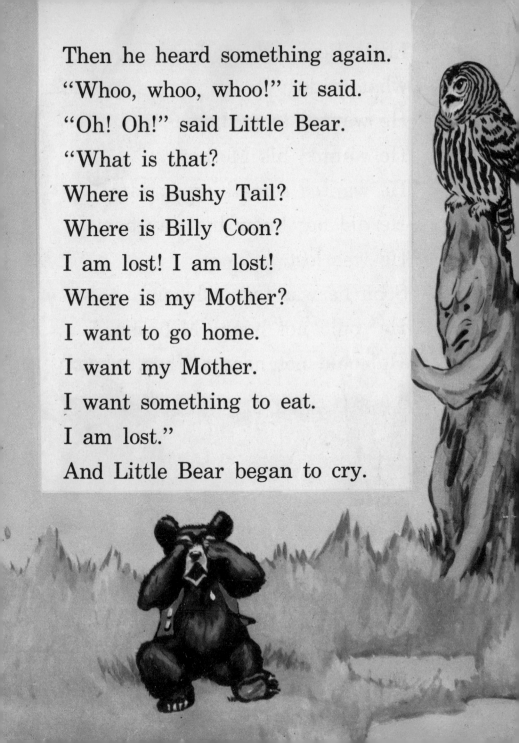

Then he heard something again.

"Whoo, whoo, whoo!" it said.

"Oh! Oh!" said Little Bear.

"What is that?

Where is Bushy Tail?

Where is Billy Coon?

I am lost! I am lost!

Where is my Mother?

I want to go home.

I want my Mother.

I want something to eat.

I am lost."

And Little Bear began to cry.

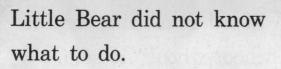

Little Bear did not know
what to do.
He wanted to go home.
He wanted his Mother.
He wanted something to eat.
He did not know his way home.
He was lost.
Soon he was fast asleep.
He could not hear "Moo, moo."
He could not hear "Whoo, whoo."

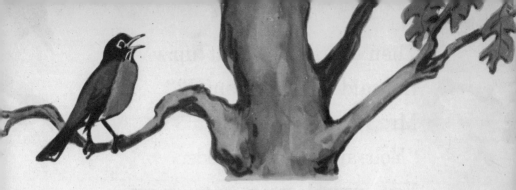

Wake Up, Little Bear

Mr. Robin was singing in a tree.

He said, "Wake up! Wake up!

It is morning! It is morning!

Come, Little Bear, come.

You were asleep for a long time.

You were lost, Little Bear.

Wake up! Wake up!

It is morning!"

Then Little Bear sat up.
He said, "Where am I?"
Mr. Robin said,
"You are in the woods.
You were lost.
You were asleep for a long time."
Billy Coon said,
"Good morning, Little Bear."
Bushy Tail said,
"Good morning, Little Bear.
We have come to play with you."
Little Bear was happy now.

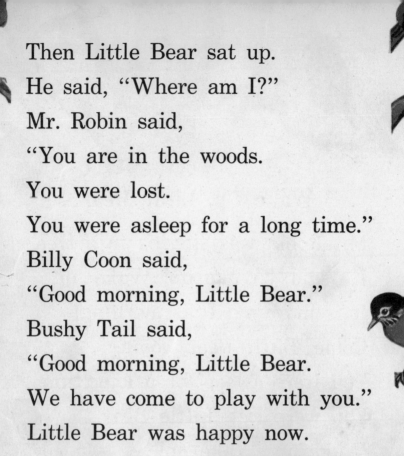

Billy Coon said,
"Can you stay and play with us?"
"Oh, no!" said Little Bear.
"Mother wants me to come home
But I can not find the way home.
Will you help me find my way?
Mother will be happy to see you.
She will give you some honey."
Billy Coon said, "Come with us.
We will help you."

A BIRTHDAY

Anne's Birthday

Tomorrow is Anne's birthday.

The cake is for Anne.

Nancy said, "Mother! Mother!

May we buy something for Anne?

May we go to the store?

We want to buy a toy for her."

Mother said, "You may buy a toy.

You may go to the store."

At the Store

Bob said, "May we see the toys?
We want a toy for Anne.
Tomorrow is her birthday."
The man said,
"You may look at all the toys."
Nancy said, "Oh, look, Bob!
Here is a toy lamb."
Bob said, "Here is a train.
And here are some soldiers.
See this drum!
Boom, boom, boom!"

A Doll

The man said, "Here is a doll.
This doll can cry.
Anne will like this doll."
Bob said, "Anne will like
a doll that can cry.
Let us buy the doll, Nancy.
We can surprise Anne
with a doll that can cry."

"Oh, Mother!" said Nancy.
"Can you guess what we have?
Guess what is in this box."
Mother laughed and said,
"That looks like a doll box."
"Where can we put it?" said Bob.
"We do not want Anne to find it.
We want to surprise her."
"I know! I know!" said Nancy.
"Let us put it under the table.
Anne will not find it there."

97

The Birthday Fun

Anne said, "Oh! Oh!
See my birthday cake!
I want to give some
cake to my doll."
Anne is so happy.
She has a doll that can cry.
She has a birthday cake, too.
Father has something for her.
He will give it to her
after dinner.

Father said, "Come, Anne,
Here is something for you."
Anne said, "Oh! A story book!
Read to me! Read to me!
Please read a story to me."
Mother said, "Read one story.
Then it will be time for bed."
Father said, "I will read
The Candy Dog story."

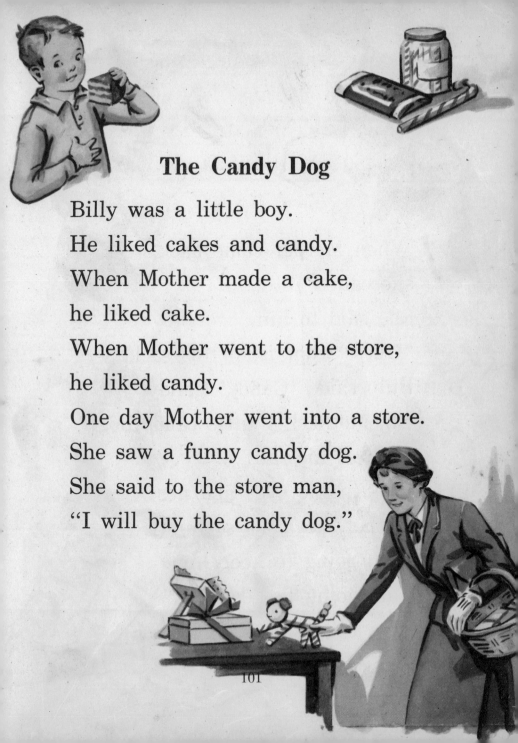

The Candy Dog

Billy was a little boy.

He liked cakes and candy.

When Mother made a cake,

he liked cake.

When Mother went to the store,

he liked candy.

One day Mother went into a store.

She saw a funny candy dog.

She said to the store man,

"I will buy the candy dog."

When Mother came back,
she called Billy.
She said to him,
"Guess what is in this sack."
Billy said, "Candy! Candy!
Oh, Mother! A little candy dog!
Look at his tail.
Look at his eyes and nose.
Mother, he looks so funny.
I am going to keep him.
I am going to keep him
for a long time."

Billy looked at his candy dog.

He wanted to eat him.

He looked and looked

at the candy dog's tail.

He said, "Oh, Little Dog!

Your tail is too long.

Your tail is too long.

I will eat just a little

of your long tail."

And he did.

He ate the candy dog's tail.

"Now," said Billy,

"I am going to put you away.

I am going to keep you."

But Billy did not put him away.
He looked at him again.
He said, "Your legs look funny.
Candy Dog, I ate your tail.
I am going to eat just one leg.
No! I will eat them all.
I will eat all of your legs."
And he did.
He ate the candy dog's legs.
"Now," said Billy,
"I am going to put you away.
I am going to keep you."

But Billy did not put him away.

He looked at him again.

He said, "Little Candy Dog,

you look very funny.

You have no tail—I ate it.

You have no legs—I ate them.

You can not walk.

You can not talk.

I am going to eat you up"

And he did.

He ate the candy dog.

Candy dogs are made to eat.

They are not made to keep.

THE CIRCUS IS COMING

CIRCUS

This is the Circus!
Oh, what fun! What fun!

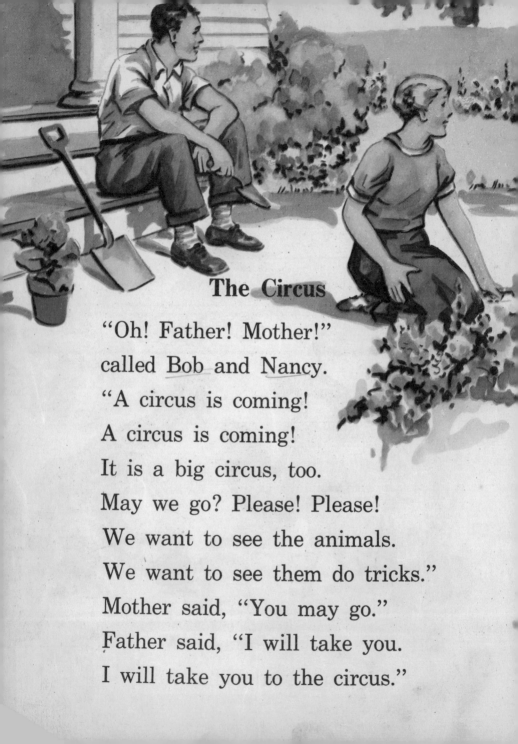

The Circus

"Oh! Father! Mother!"
called Bob and Nancy.
"A circus is coming!
A circus is coming!
It is a big circus, too.
May we go? Please! Please!
We want to see the animals.
We want to see them do tricks."
Mother said, "You may go."
Father said, "I will take you.
I will take you to the circus."

"Oh, Mother!" said Bob.
"May we ask Jack and Jean
to go to the circus?
May we ask them to go with us?
They want to see the circus.
They want to see the animals.
The animals will do tricks."
Mother said, "Yes, Bob.
You may ask them."
So Bob wrote a letter.
He wrote to Jack and Jean.

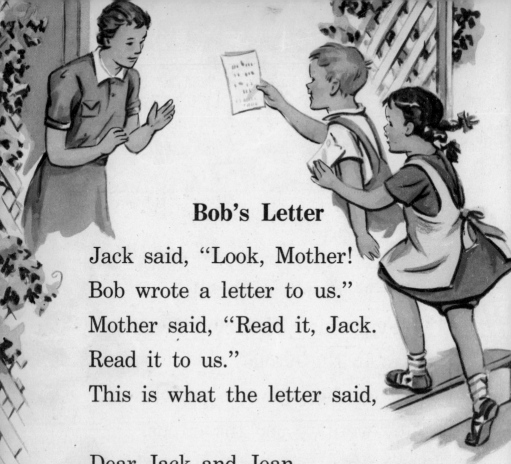

Bob's Letter

Jack said, "Look, Mother!
Bob wrote a letter to us."
Mother said, "Read it, Jack.
Read it to us."
This is what the letter said,

Dear Jack and Jean,
We want you to come to see us.
Can you come Saturday morning?
We have a surprise for you.

Good-by,

Bob and Nancy

Jack and Jean ran to Father.

Jean said, "Here is a letter.

It is from Bob and Nancy.

They want us to come Saturday.

Please may we go, Father?

Will you take us in the car

Saturday morning?"

Father said, "I can not take you

in the car Saturday.

You may go on the bus.

I will come for you in the car."

Jean said, "The bus! The bus!

Oh! I like to ride on the bus."

On the Bus

It is Saturday morning.

Jack and Jean are happy.

They are on the bus.

Jean said, "Guess what I see."

Jack said, "Is it a train?"

Jean said, "It is not a train.

But it can go fast."

"Oh!" said Jack.

"I see that airplane, too."

"Guess what I see," said Jack.

"It can not walk.

But it can go."

Jean said, "Can it go high?"

Jack said, "It can not go high."

Jean said, "Oh, I know!

It is the boat in the water."

Jack laughed and said,

"Two boats!"

Hello! Hello!

"Hello, Bob! Hello, Nancy!"
said Jack and Jean.
Bob and Nancy said, "Hello!
We are glad to see you.
We are glad you could come."
Jean said, "We are glad, too.
What is the surprise?"
Bob said, "The circus!
Father is going to take us
to the circus."

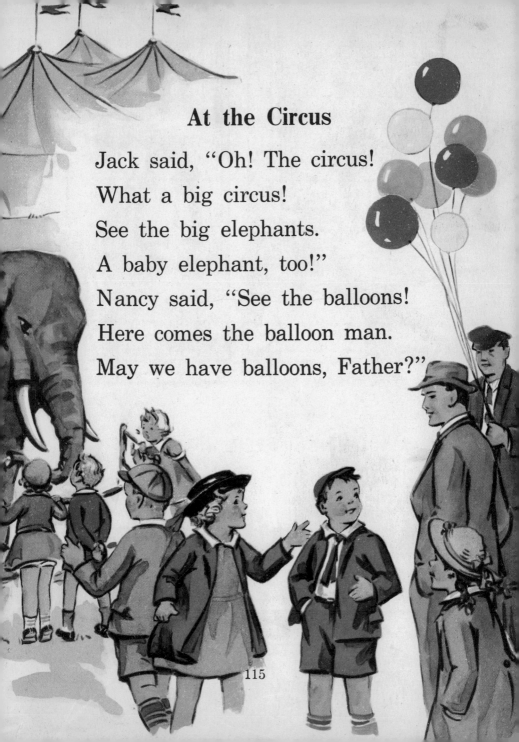

At the Circus

Jack said, "Oh! The circus!

What a big circus!

See the big elephants.

A baby elephant, too!"

Nancy said, "See the balloons!

Here comes the balloon man.

May we have balloons, Father?"

116

After the Circus

"Oh, Mother!" said Nancy.
"We had a good time.
We saw big elephants.
We saw a baby elephant, too."
Jean said, "A clown had a pony.
But he could not ride him."
Bob said, "One clown had a dog.
The dog could do tricks."

Father said, "Did you like
that little dog with the clown?
That little dog is called Frisk.
Here is a story about him.
It is in the paper.
It tells about Frisk.
He had one good friend."

Here is the story about Frisk.

Frisk, a Little Dog

Frisk was a little dog.
He was black and white.
He had no home.
He had no bed.
He had no one to feed him.
He was a good little dog.
And he had just one friend.
This friend was the postman.

Frisk saw the postman
every morning.
He said, "Bow-wow, bow-wow."
He was glad to see the postman.
The postman was his friend.
One morning the postman
lost a paper.
Frisk saw him drop the paper.
So he ran to get it.
He took it to the postman.

The postman said, "Thank you.
Thank you, Frisk.
You are a good dog."
Then the postman threw a paper.
He said, "Get it, Frisk!"
Frisk ran to get it.
He took it back to the postman.
Every day the postman
threw a paper for Frisk to get.
Every day Frisk did this trick.

A Circus Dog

One day a circus came.

There were many animals.

There were monkeys.

There were elephants and tigers.

There were clowns, too.

There were many, many balloons.

Frisk jumped up and down.

He jumped around and said,

"Bow-wow, bow-wow, bow-wow."

The postman saw Frisk.

He said, "Come Frisk! Come!

Are you afraid of the circus?"

Frisk was not afraid.
He liked the circus.
One clown threw papers
to the boys and girls.
Frisk ran to get the papers.
He took them back to the clown.
The clown threw papers again
Frisk ran to get them.
The clown had a little car.
Frisk jumped into it.
He sat up in the little car.
The boys and girls laughed.

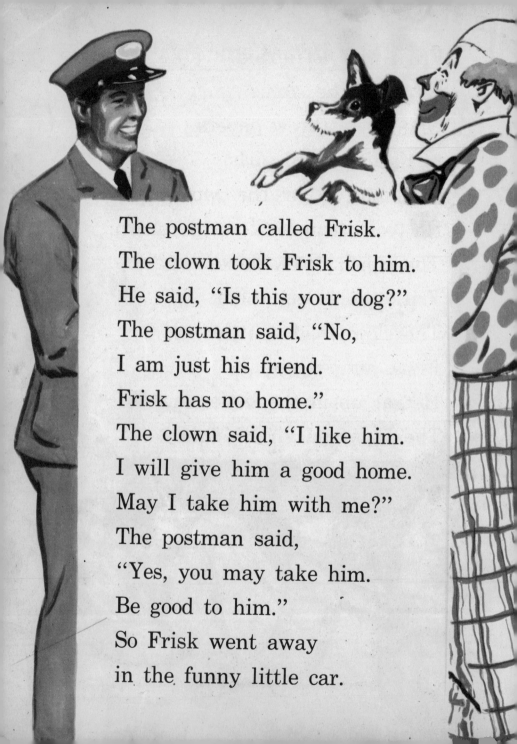

The postman called Frisk.
The clown took Frisk to him.
He said, "Is this your dog?"
The postman said, "No,
I am just his friend.
Frisk has no home."
The clown said, "I like him.
I will give him a good home.
May I take him with me?"
The postman said,
"Yes, you may take him.
Be good to him."
So Frisk went away
in the funny little car.

The Circus Came Again

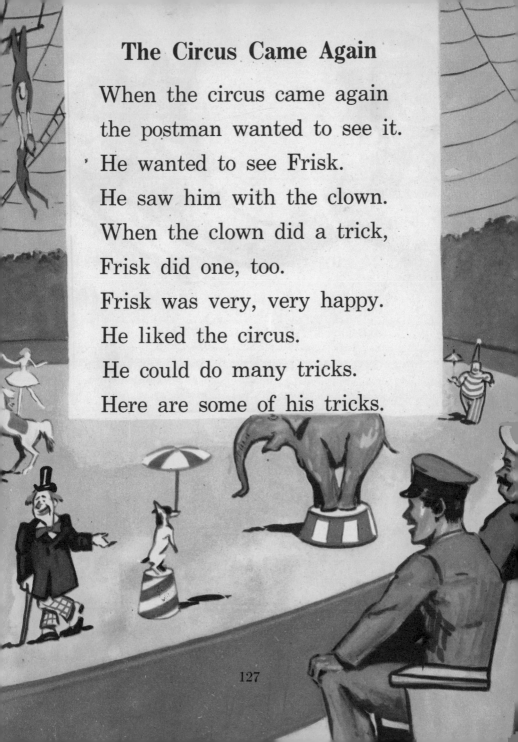

When the circus came again
the postman wanted to see it.
He wanted to see Frisk.
He saw him with the clown.
When the clown did a trick,
Frisk did one, too.
Frisk was very, very happy.
He liked the circus.
He could do many tricks.
Here are some of his tricks.

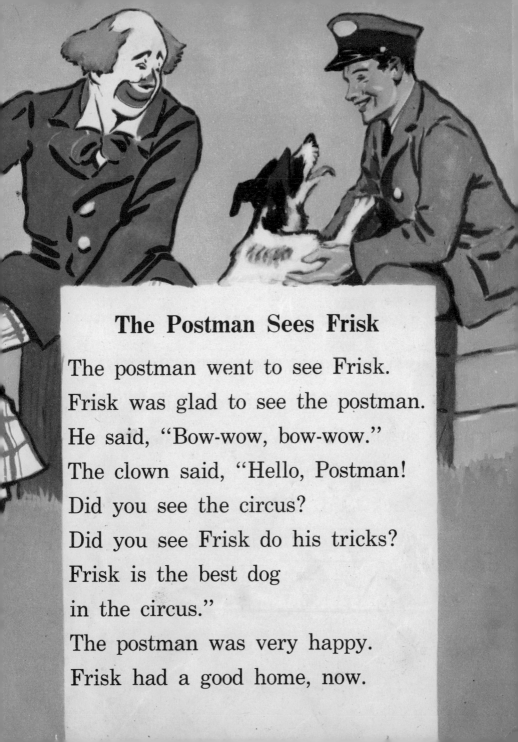

The Postman Sees Frisk

The postman went to see Frisk.

Frisk was glad to see the postman.

He said, "Bow-wow, bow-wow."

The clown said, "Hello, Postman!

Did you see the circus?

Did you see Frisk do his tricks?

Frisk is the best dog

in the circus."

The postman was very happy.

Frisk had a good home, now.

Going Home

"Here comes Father," said Jack.
"He is coming to take us home."
Jean said, "We had a good time
at the circus."
Jack said, "Thank you
for the good time at the circus.
Good-by, Nancy and Bob."
"Good-by, good-by," said Jean.
"Come and see us soon."

Back Home at the Farm

Mother said, "What did you see
at the circus?"
Jack and Jean said,
"Elephants! Tigers!
Clowns! Balloons!"
Father said, "What did
you like best at the circus?"
Jean said,
"I liked the clowns best."
Jack said,
"I liked the animals best.
I liked the elephants."

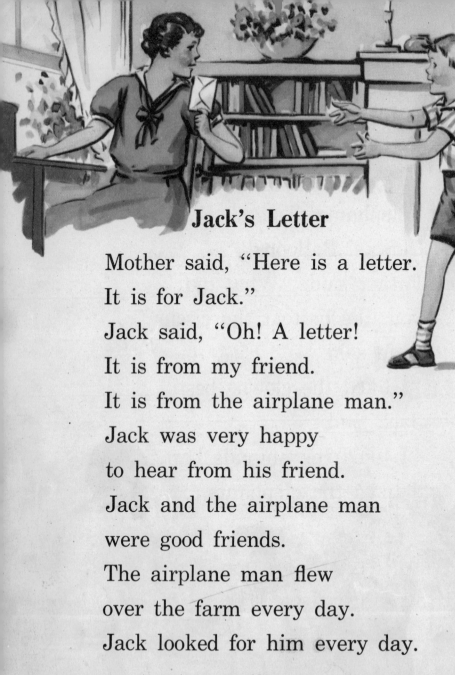

Jack's Letter

Mother said, "Here is a letter.
It is for Jack."
Jack said, "Oh! A letter!
It is from my friend.
It is from the airplane man."
Jack was very happy
to hear from his friend.
Jack and the airplane man
were good friends.
The airplane man flew
over the farm every day.
Jack looked for him every day.

Mother said, "Open it, Jack.
He may be coming to see us."
Jack opened his letter.
This was what the letter said.
Dear Jack,

I will fly over your farm
tomorrow morning. I have
something for you. I will
drop it to you from the
airplane. You can see me
drop it.

> Good-by,
> Your friend,
> The airplane man.

When morning came
Jack was very happy.
He looked up many, many times.
Then he heard the airplane.
He said, "Oh, I hear it!
I hear the airplane.
I want to see my friend.
I want to see him
drop something for me."
He ran as fast as he could.

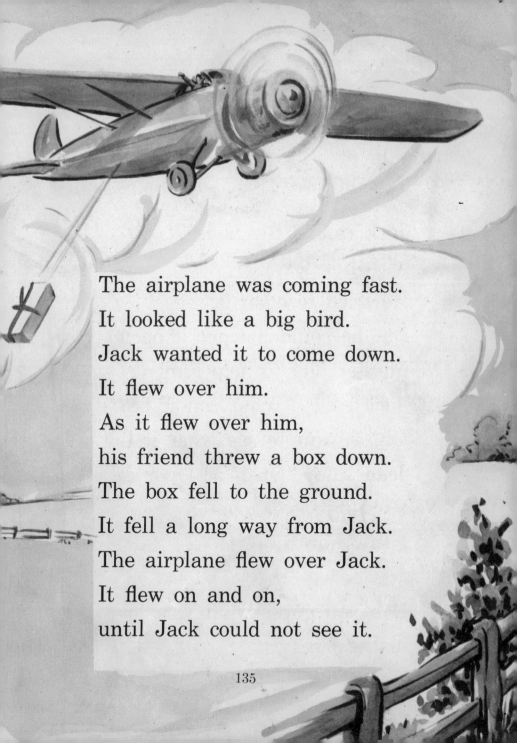

The airplane was coming fast.
It looked like a big bird.
Jack wanted it to come down.
It flew over him.
As it flew over him,
his friend threw a box down.
The box fell to the ground.
It fell a long way from Jack.
The airplane flew over Jack.
It flew on and on,
until Jack could not see it.

Jack ran to the house
with his box.
He tried to open it.
But he could not get it open.
Mother had to help him.
Jack said, "What can it be?
Oh! I want to see what it is!"
Jean said, "Open it! Open it!
I want to see, too.
I saw him drop it."

Can you guess what was
in the box? *a little toy
airplane;*

A little toy airplane!

It was just like the big one
his friend had.
It was red and blue and
it could fly.
Jack said, "Oh, Mother!
It is just what I wanted.
A little airplane!
I can make it fly and fly."

Trigger and the Bee

Trigger was a little dog.

He had come to live at the farm.

He played all day long.

He ran after the hens.

He ran after the chicks.

He ran after the pigs.

What fun he had!

He liked to see them run.

One day Trigger was
in his little house.
He was not asleep.
He heard, "Buzz, buzz, buzz, buzz."
His head came up.
He looked all around.
Then he jumped up.
He wanted to know
what made that "Buzz, buzz."

Trigger ran out of his house.

He heard, "Buzz, buzz, buzz."

He saw what made that, "Buzz."

He wanted to play with it.

He tried to catch it.

He jumped and jumped after it.

He went around and around.

He wanted to play.

Now Trigger did not know
that a bee said, "Buzz, buzz."
He tried and tried to catch it.
And he did.
He wanted to smell it.
He put his nose on it.
Then Oh! Oh! Oh!
Do you know what the bee did
to Trigger's nose? The bee
stog Trigger.

Trigger's nose was as big
as his nose could be.
He did not like to hear,
"Buzz, buzz, buzz."
And he did not like little bees!

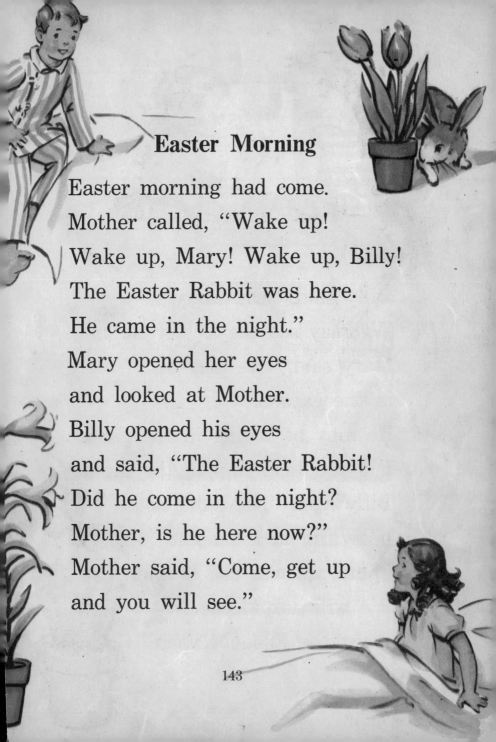

Easter Morning

Easter morning had come.
Mother called, "Wake up!
Wake up, Mary! Wake up, Billy!
The Easter Rabbit was here.
He came in the night."
Mary opened her eyes
and looked at Mother.
Billy opened his eyes
and said, "The Easter Rabbit!
Did he come in the night?
Mother, is he here now?"
Mother said, "Come, get up
and you will see."

Billy said, "Oh, Mary!
We may see the Easter Rabbit."
Mary said, "He may be
in the garden.
He may be hiding in the garden.
Did you hear him in the night?"
Billy said, "No, I did not
hear him in the night.
Come, we will ask Mother.
We will ask Mother
about the Easter Rabbit."

"Mother! Mother!" said Mary.
"Did you see the Easter Rabbit?
Did you see him in the night?
Is he here now, Mother?"
Mother said, "He may be.
He may be hiding from you."
Mary looked all around.
She wanted to find him.

145

Just then Billy called,
"Oh, come here, Mary!
See what I have found.
I have found something pretty."
Mary said, "What is it, Billy?
Have you found
the Easter Rabbit?"
"No," said Billy, "I have
not found the Easter Rabbit.
But see what I have found."

"Oh! Oh!" said Mary.

"See the two pretty baskets.

One basket is for Billy.

One basket is for me."

Billy said,

"The Easter Rabbit wrote letters."

Billy opened his letter.

Mary opened her letter, too.

She said, "Oh, Mother!

This is what he wrote to me."

Dear Mary,

Please go to the garden

and open your eyes.

Look all around, Mary.

You may find a surprise.

The Easter Rabbit

Dear Billy,

Good-by, Billy dear.

I wish I could stay.

Be a good boy, Billy.

I will come back some day.

The Easter Rabbit

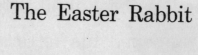

They took their baskets
and ran into the garden.
Billy said, "I wish
I could find the Easter Rabbit."
Mary said, "I wish
we could find him, too.
He may be hiding here."
Just then Mary saw something.
She said, "Come here, Billy.
Come and see the Easter eggs."

149

Billy said, "Come here, Mary.
Come and see my surprise."
Billy had found two nests.
In the nests were Easter eggs.
They were yellow, blue, and red.
Mary said, "Easter eggs.
See all the Easter eggs!
Let us put them in our baskets."

Mary said, "Look at our baskets.
And look at all our eggs.
The Easter Rabbit was here.
He was in our garden.
He was good to us.
I wish I could find him."
Billy said,
"I wish we could, too.
I wish we could find him.
Then we could thank him."

WORD LIST

The following list contains the 165 words introduced in the First Reader, Level One.

The 49 starred words have been developed in Primer, Level Two, but are introduced as new words in this First Reader, Level One.

The basic words are all found in standard word lists and in meaningful vocabulary lists for the first grade. Omitting the 6 proper names and the 5 words, (wiggle, boom, jack-in-the-box, ker-chug, and whoo), there are 154 words, or 100 per cent, in Gates revised word list.

The ease of this book is shown by:

59 pages with 0 new words   29 pages with 2 new words
41 pages with 1 new word   22 pages with 3 new words

1		17	laughed	34	birds	58	
2	wiggle		water*		back	59	tiptoed
	tail*	18	their		soon	60	
3	again		let*	35		61	sat*
	know	19		36	tree*	62	knock
	rabbit*	20		37	eggs*		no*
4	swim	21	his*	38	rain*		voice*
	turtle*		hat	39	her	63	bear*
5	give	22	were	40	ker-chug		honey
6		23		41			bee
7	came*	24	tomorrow	42		64	
	from		sleds	43	book	65	until
8			surprise	44	singing	66	climb*
9	afraid	25	pull*	45	robin		began
	of	26		46	nest*	67	Bushy*
	puppy	27		47	fly		squirrel*
10	about	28	put	48	bring	68	climbed
	who		long		yes	69	Billy
	hear*		nose		your*		Coon
11	corn	29	near*	49		70	
	Mrs.*		jumped	50	eat*	71	hole
	some	30	eyes*		apples	72	tried
12	so		stay*	51			reach
13	could		black*	52	chairs		high
	then	31	sun	53	way	73	
14			joke		that*	74	
15	crying*		Mr.*	54	hiding	75	buzz
	just*	32		55		76	cry
16	tell	33	spring	56	smells	77	
	something*			57			

78 dinner
79
80
81 woods
    into
82
83 heard*
    moo
84
85
86
87 whoo
    lost
88 asleep*
89 morning
    wake*
90
91
92
93
94 buy
    store
95 drum*
    soldiers*
    boom*
96
97 box
98
99
100 please
    candy
    dog*
101 liked
    when
    day

102 called
    sack*
    keep
103 ate
104 leg*
105 very
106 circus
    coming
107
108 animals
    take
    tricks
109 ask
    wrote
    letter
110 dear
    Saturday
111 car
    bus
112
113
114 glad
    hello
115 elephant*
116
117
118
119 clown
120 paper
    Frisk
    friend
121 white*
    postman
122 drop
    took
    every

123 threw
124 tigers*
    many
125
126
127
128
129 best*
130
131
132 flew
    over
133 opened
    open
134
135 fell*
    ground*
136
137
138 Trigger
139 head*
140
141
142
143 Easter
    Mary
    night
    garden
144
145
146 found
147 basket
148 wish*
149
150
151

VOCABULARY TABLE

| Pre-Primers | | | Primers | | First Reader |
Level I	Level II	Level III	Level I	Level II	Level I
Basic Words 52	52	52	52	46	52
	New Words 15	5	15	10	15
	67				
		New Words 8	8	4	8
		65			
			New Words 81	75	79
			156		
				New Words 63	49
				198	
					New Words 116
					319

This table shows the cumulative and repetitive vocabulary of each book in the series through the First Reader, Level One. Reading down the steps of the table the new words of each book are shown. Reading across the table the repetition of words is shown. For example: All 52 words introduced in Pre-Primer, Level One are repeated in Pre-Primers, Levels Two and Three and in Primer, Level One; 46 of them are repeated in Primer, Level Two; and all 52 are repeated in First Reader, Level One; etc.

ACKNOWLEDGMENTS

Grateful acknowledgment is made to the following authors and publishers for special permission to make adaptations from copyrighted materials:

To Elise Reid Boylston for "Guess What Bob Has" and "A Good Little Bear." To the Whitman Publishing Company for "Jack's Letter" adapted from "The Mail Plane" from *It's Fun to Read, and Work and Play*. To Rand McNally for "Frisk, A Little Dog," adapted from "Fritz, the Little Tramp Dog," by Elizabeth Gale from *Circus Animals*. To Saalfield Publishing Company for "A Candy Dog" adapted from "The Sugar Dog" from *Read To Me Stories*. For "Easter Morning" from *Happily Ever After* by Catherine Beebe, 1938, by permission of Thomas Nelson & Sons, New York.